POPULARMMOS

Popular MMOs (aka Pat) is one of the most popular
YouTubers in the world. Pat and his wife, Jen (aka
Gaming With Jen), created their *Minecraft*–inspired
channel, PopularMMOS, in 2012. Since then, they
have entertained millions of fans around the world
with their gaming videos and original characters.

Pat and Jen live in Florida with their cat, Cloud.
PopularMMOS Presents: Enter the Mine is their
second book.

To my Nana. Can't wait for our next adventure.—D.J.

A special thanks to Joe Caramagna for all his creative help!

Library of Congress Control Number: 2018966562
ISBN 978-0-06-289428-1 (trade bdg.)
ISBN 978-0-06-291529-0 (special edition)
ISBN 978-0-06-294024-7 (special edition)
ISBN 978-0-06-293357-7 (special edition)
ISBN 978-0-06-295022-2 (special edition)

The artist used an iPad Pro and the app Procreate to create the digital illustrations for this book.
Typography by Erica De Chavez 19 20 21 22 23 PC/LSCC 10 9 8 7 6 5 4 3 2 1 ❖ First Edition

POPULARMMOS

PRESENTS

ENTER THE MINE

By **PAT+JEN** from **POPULARMMOS**
Illustrated by **DANI JONES**

HARPER
An Imprint of HarperCollinsPublishers

Hey, what's going on, guys!

It's Pat and Jen, and we're so thrilled that you're reading our second book. It's another exciting adventure where you'll get to meet all your favorite characters from our YouTube channel. Of course, there's me and Jen and Bomby and Cloud, but this time, Bob, Hoss, the Mayor, Valentine, and more get in on the action. We all band together to stop Evil Jen's evilest plot yet—and worse, this time she has Evil Pat along for the ride!

We can't tell you how much we appreciate your support. Writing this book has been a totally amazing experience, and we can't wait to tell you how much it means to us both that you've decided to Enter the Mine along with us. We think you'll really enjoy this "explosive" new adventure—watch out for all the zombies and holes. We just hope you enjoy reading it as much as we enjoyed writing it. Being creative is what we are all about, and we hope that this book inspires you to be creative, too!

Have fun! Read on! And thanks for being a fan.

PAT & JEN

Pat is an awesome dude who's always looking for an epic adventure with his partner, the Super Girly Gamer Jen. Pat loves to have fun with his friends and take control of every situation with his cool weapons and can-do attitude. Jen is the sweetest person in the world and loves to laugh, but don't let her cheeriness fool you—she's also fierce. In fact, she could be an even greater adventurer than Pat . . . if she weren't so clumsy. Together, along with their cat, Cloud, they have a bond that can never be broken.

CARTER

Carter is Jen's best friend and biggest fan, but he doesn't seem to like Pat very much at all. Carter is also not very smart and sometimes carries a pickle that he thinks is a green sword!

CAPTAIN COOKIE

No one is quite sure if Captain Cookie is a real sea captain or if he just dresses the part. He doesn't seem to be very good at anything, but that doesn't stop him from bragging about how great he is! He's rude to everyone he meets but always in a funny way.

CLOUD

Cloud is Pat and Jen's white Persian cat. He may have a fluffy exterior, but underneath, he's all *savage*.

HONEY BOO BOO

Honey Boo Boo is a golem of iron on the outside but is all softy on the inside!

BOMBY

Bomby is somewhat of a pet to Pat and Jen but also Pat's best friend. You can usually find him by following the craters left by the TNT that he loves to watch explode.

THE MAYOR

The Mayor loves being the mayor and loves reminding everyone that he's the mayor, but doesn't seem to have much authority over anyone or anything.

VALENTINE

An elf and a master archer, he leads the revolt against Evil Jen's rule in the Underworld.

BOB

Bob is Valentine's best friend. After he is imprisoned by Evil Jen, he becomes the unofficial leader of the miners.

HOSS

Hoss claims to be a doctor but doesn't seem to know anything about what a doctor actually does. He's better at being a chef. Actually, he's better at doing anything than he is at being a doctor!

EVIL JEN

Evil Jen's favorite thing is chaos. She lives for wreaking havoc on the world. What makes her truly evil, however, is that she would take someone as sweet as Jen and become an evil version of her. She even looks *exactly* like her (just don't tell Jen we said that!).

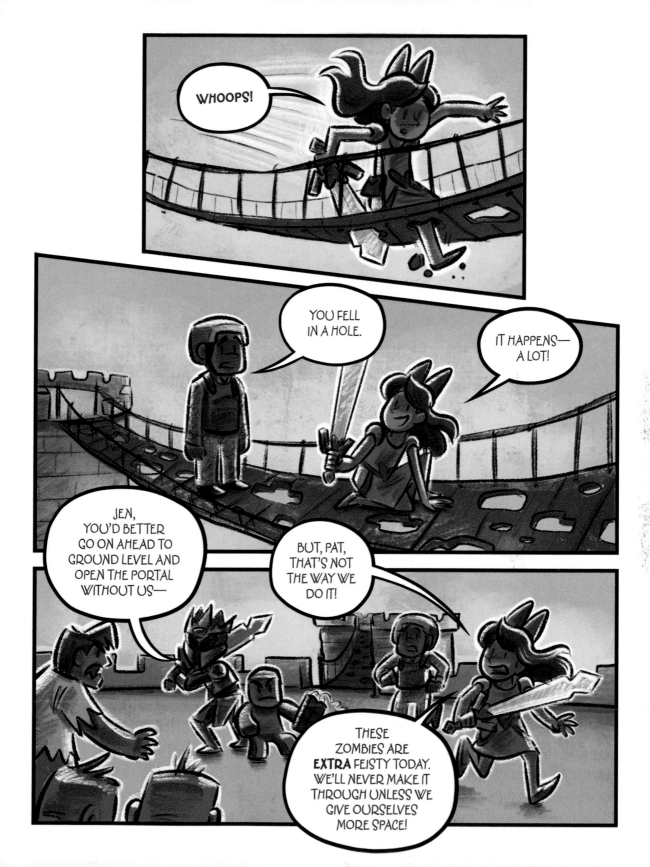

LATER...

PAT, DO YOU THINK BOMBY WILL BE ALL RIGHT?

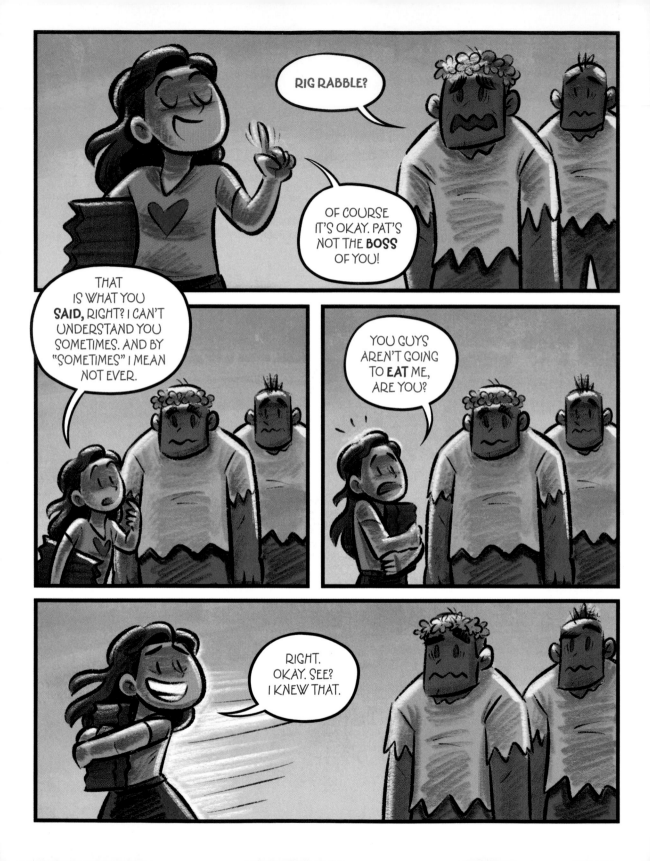

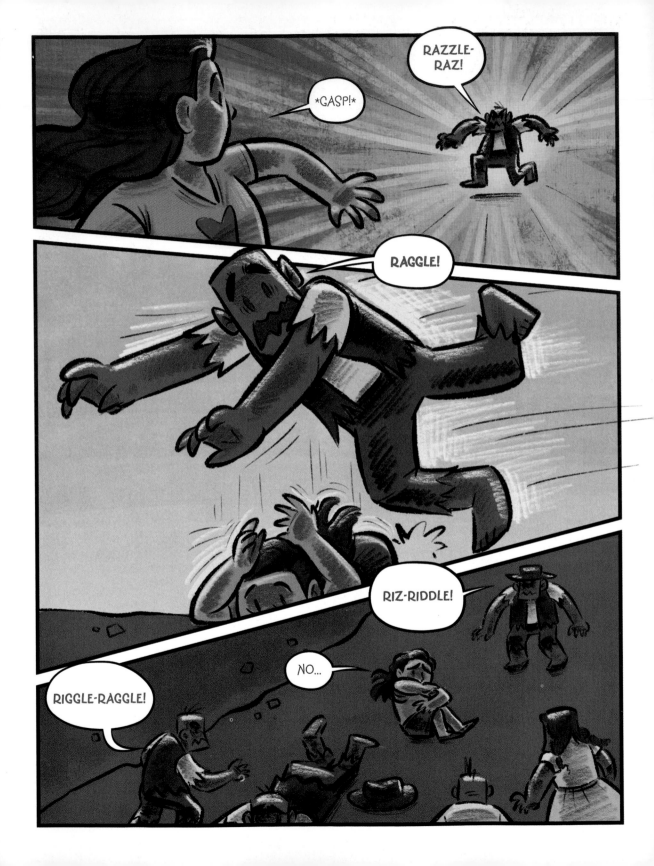

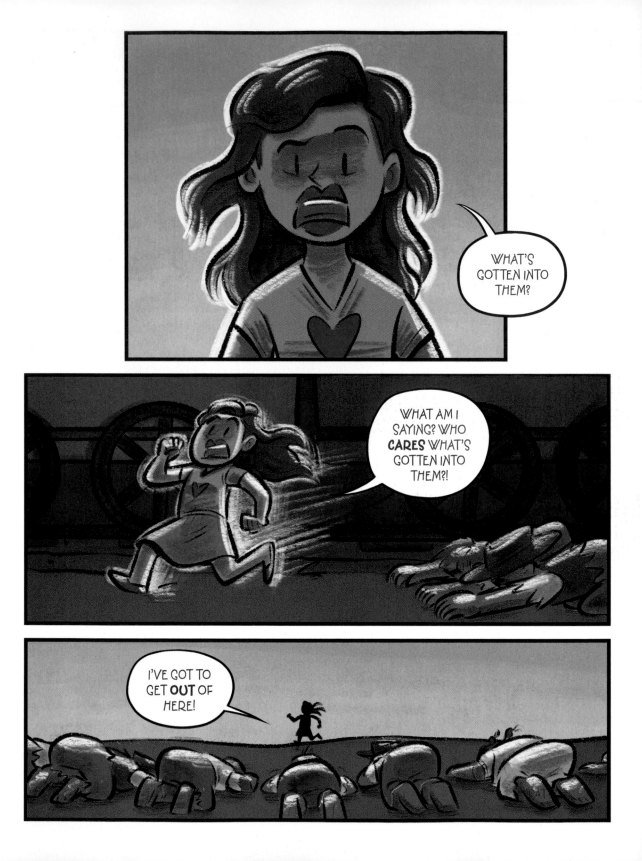

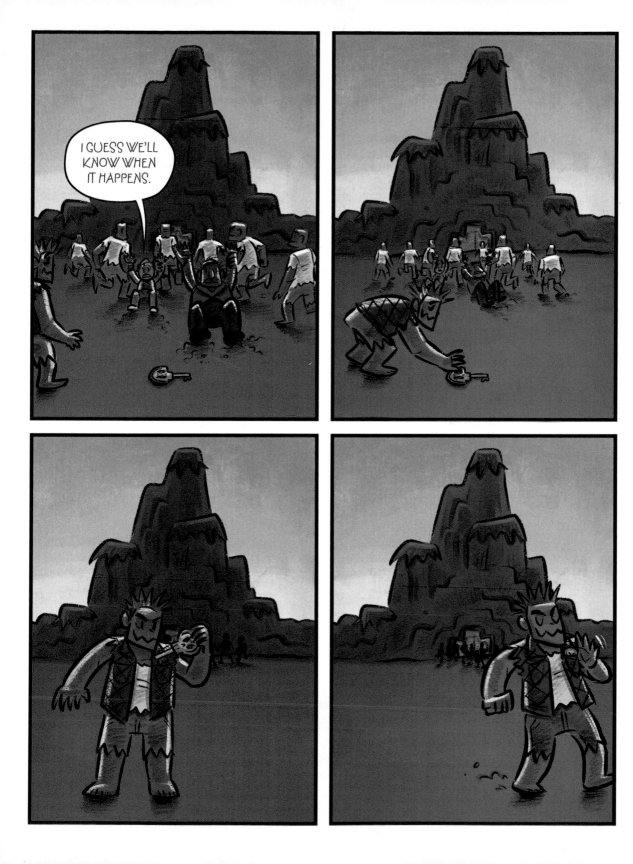

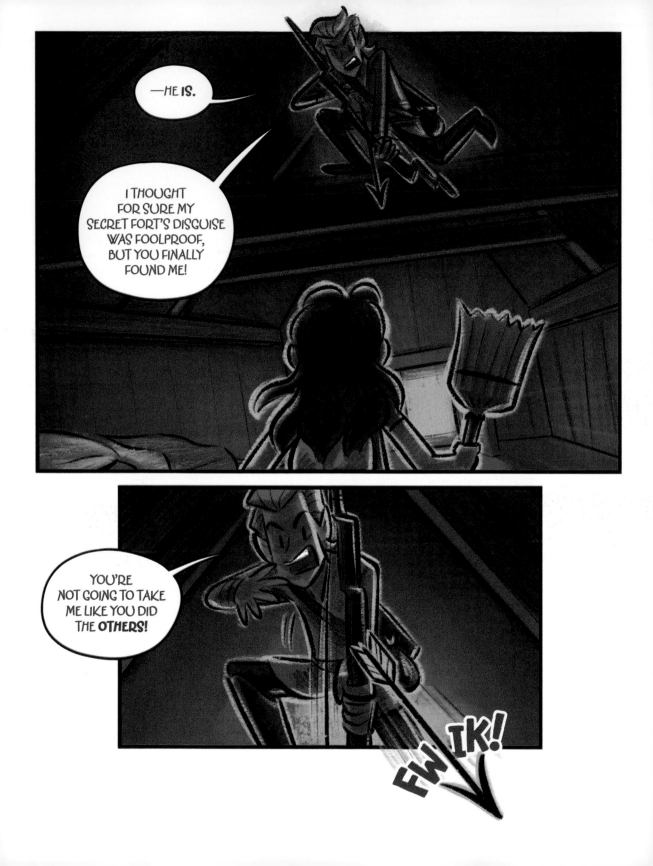

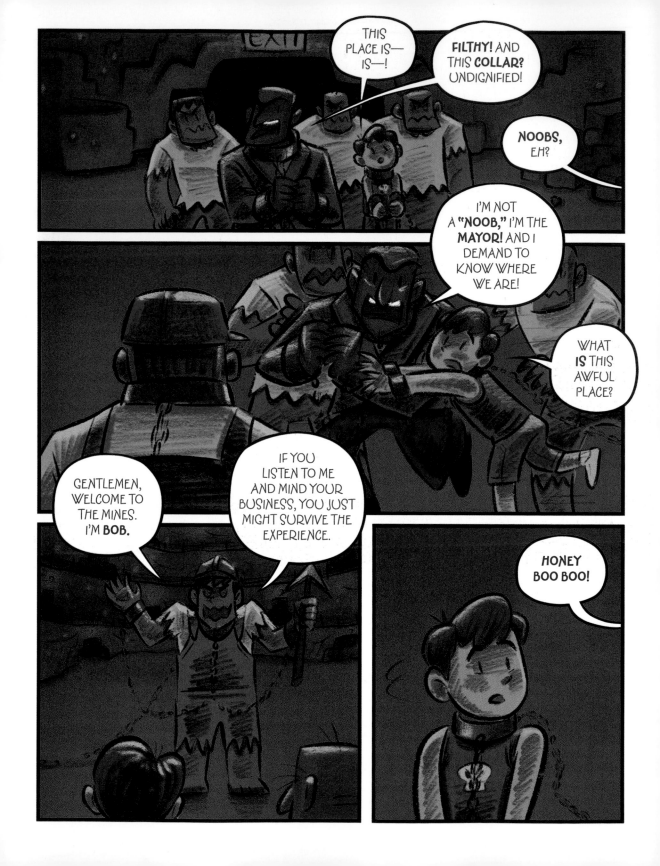

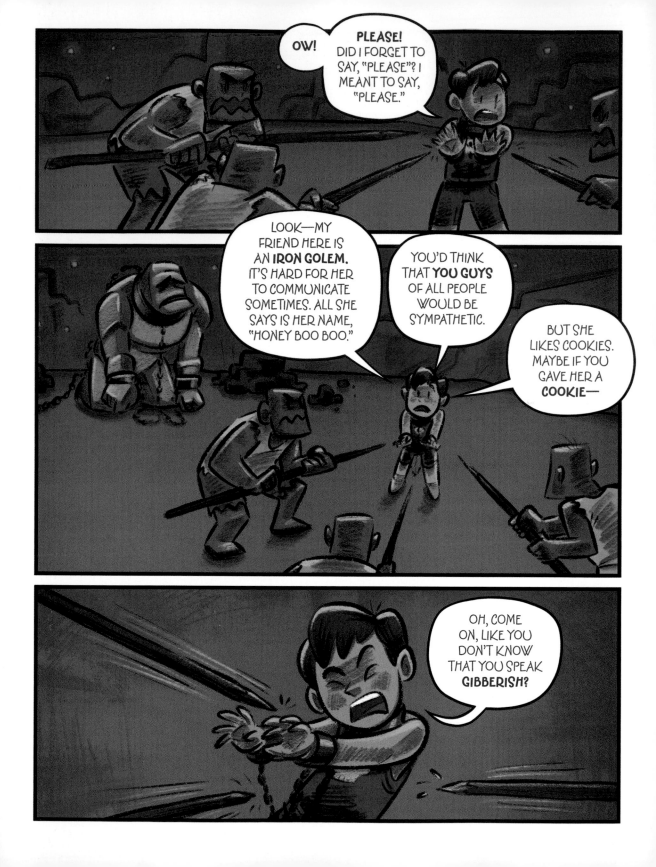

—THIS!

MAYOR!
HONEY BOO BOO!
FOLLOW M—

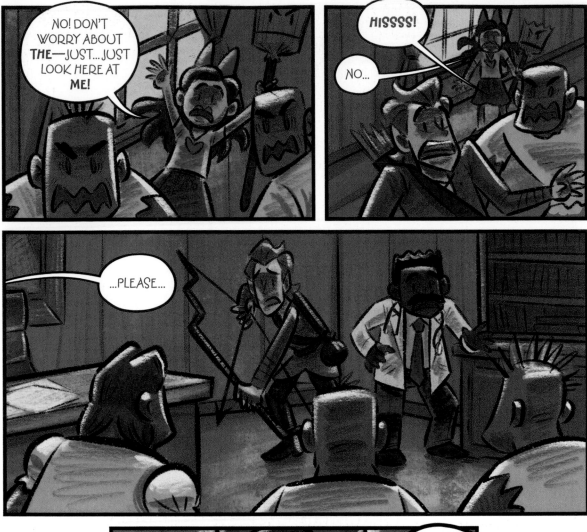

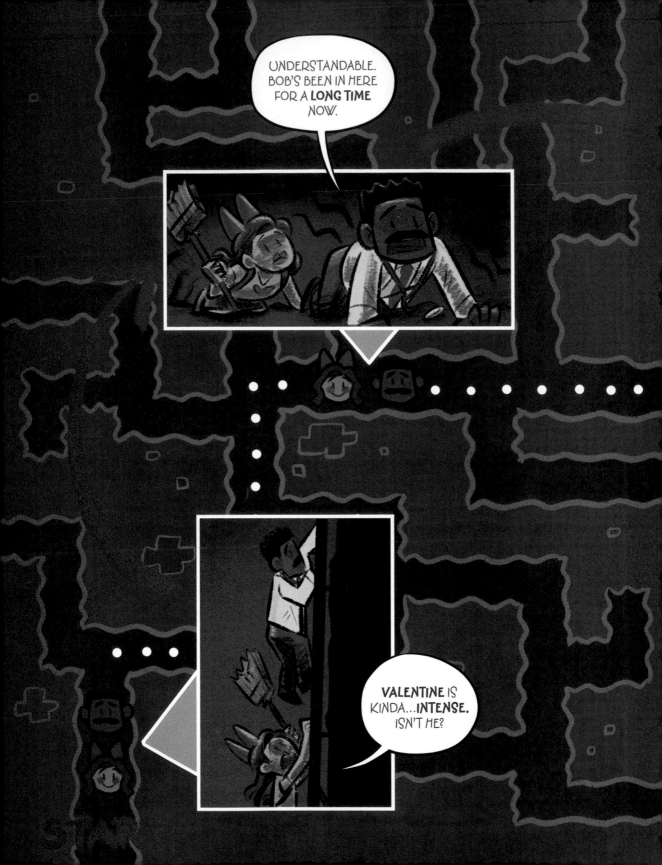

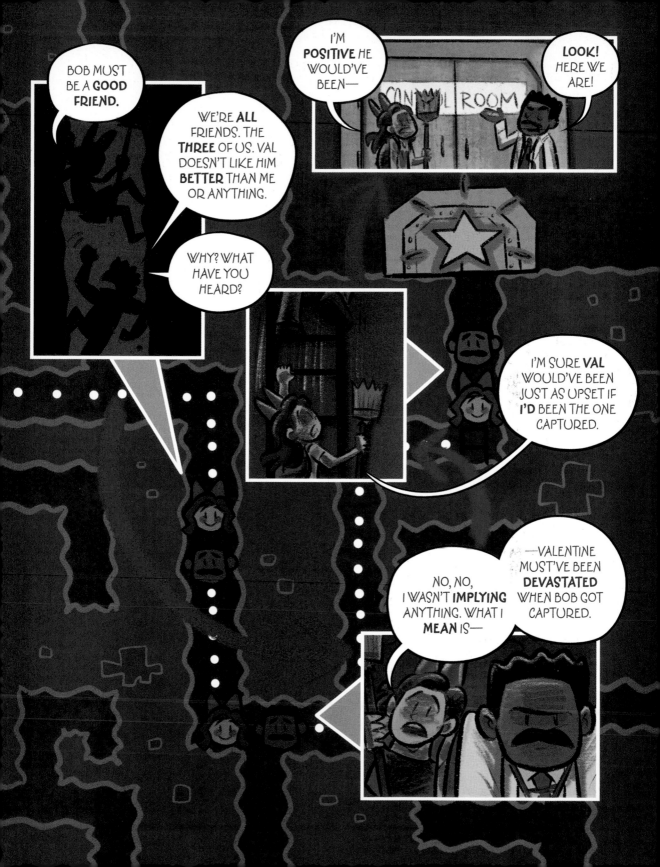

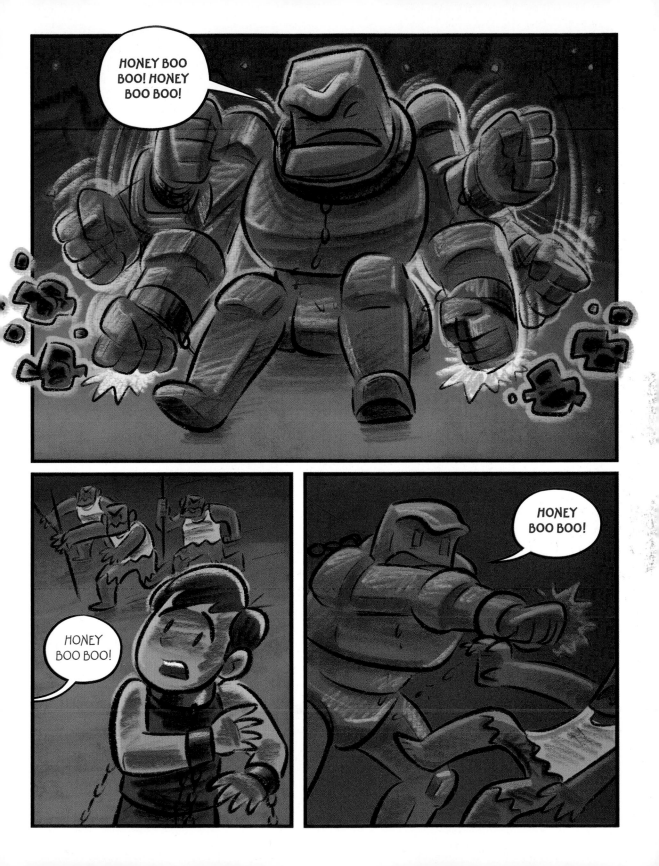

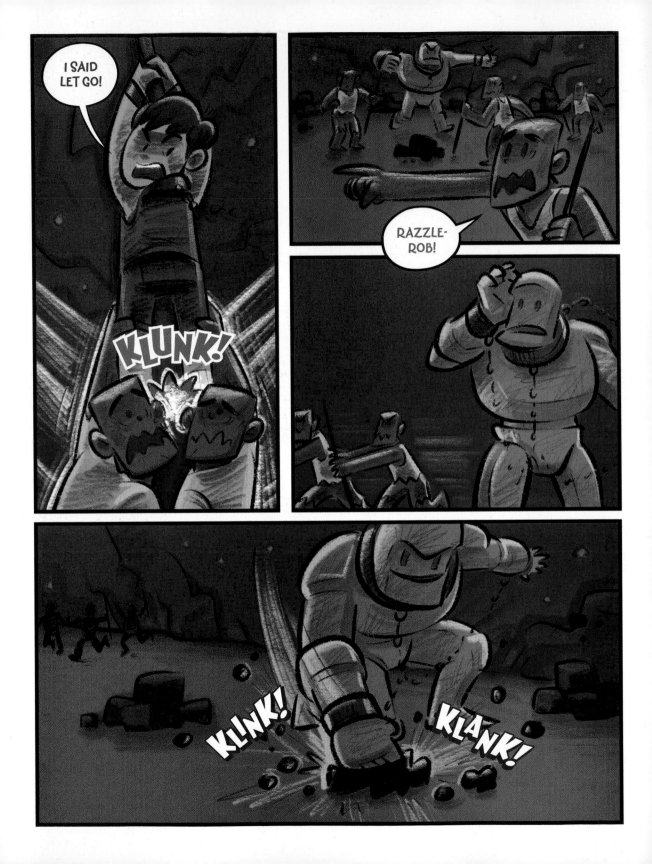

WAIT! PLEASE STOP! I—I KNOW WHO YOU ARE!

WHAT I **MEAN** IS, I KNOW THAT YOU'RE NOT JUST THE MINDLESS **EATING MACHINES** THAT EVERYONE THINKS YOU ARE. I KNOW YOU'RE JUST TRYING TO PLEASE EVIL JEN.

YOU PROBABLY LET HER BOSS YOU AROUND BECAUSE YOU DON'T HAVE THE CONFIDENCE TO MAKE YOUR **OWN** DECISIONS. BUT THAT DOESN'T MEAN YOU'RE NOT CAPABLE OF DOING STUFF.

WHAT I'M TRYING TO SAY IS, WE'RE A LOT ALIKE.

FOR **CENTURIES,** I HAVE TRIED AND **FAILED** TO BECOME THE SUPREME RULER OF **ALL** THE UNIVERSE.
WHEN MY EFFORTS LEFT ME TRAPPED IN **LIMBO,** THE SPACE BETWEEN REALITY AND THE UNDERWORLD...
...THAT AMBITION FELL TO MY FAVORITE DAUGHTER, **EVIL JEN.**
DAUGHTER?
I THOUGHT I WAS DOOMED TO LIVE IN LIMBO FOREVER! THAT SHE WAS TOO FOCUSED ON HER **FEELINGS** AND NOT THE **MISSION...**
...BUT YOU **DID** IT! YOU FOUND A WAY TO MERGE ALL WORLDS INTO **ONE** AND NOW WE WILL RULE AS WE ALWAYS MEANT TO—**TOGETHER!**